It's another great book from CGP...

Physics can be tricky. Fortunately, this book is crammed with practice questions to help you get your head around all the skills you'll need at KS3 (ages 11-14).

It's ideal if you're working at foundation level — it covers what would have been called Levels 3-6 in the old (pre-2014) Curriculum.

We've even included a **free** Online Edition you can read on your computer or tablet!

How to get your free Online Edition

Just go to **cgpbooks.co.uk/extras** and enter this code...

1588 1565 0959 2237

By the way, this code only works for one person. If somebody else has used this book before you, they might have already claimed the Online Edition.

CGP — still the best! ☺

Our sole aim here at CGP is to produce the highest quality books — carefully written, immaculately presented and dangerously close to being funny.

Then we work our socks off to get them out to you — at the cheapest possible prices.

Contents

Section 1 — Energy and Matter

Section 2 — Forces and Motion

Section 3 — Waves

Section 4 — Electricity and Magnetism

Section 5 — The Earth and Beyond

Published by CGP

Compiled by Paddy Gannon

Editors:
Gordon Henderson
Sam Pilgrim
Charlotte Whiteley
Sarah Williams

With thanks to Mark Edwards and Karen Wells for the proofreading.

ISBN: 978 1 78294 139 2

Groovy website: www.cgpbooks.co.uk

Jolly bits of clipart from CorelDRAW®
Printed by Elanders Ltd, Newcastle upon Tyne.

Forms of Energy

Q1 Draw lines to match up the **forms of energy** on the left with their correct descriptions on the right.

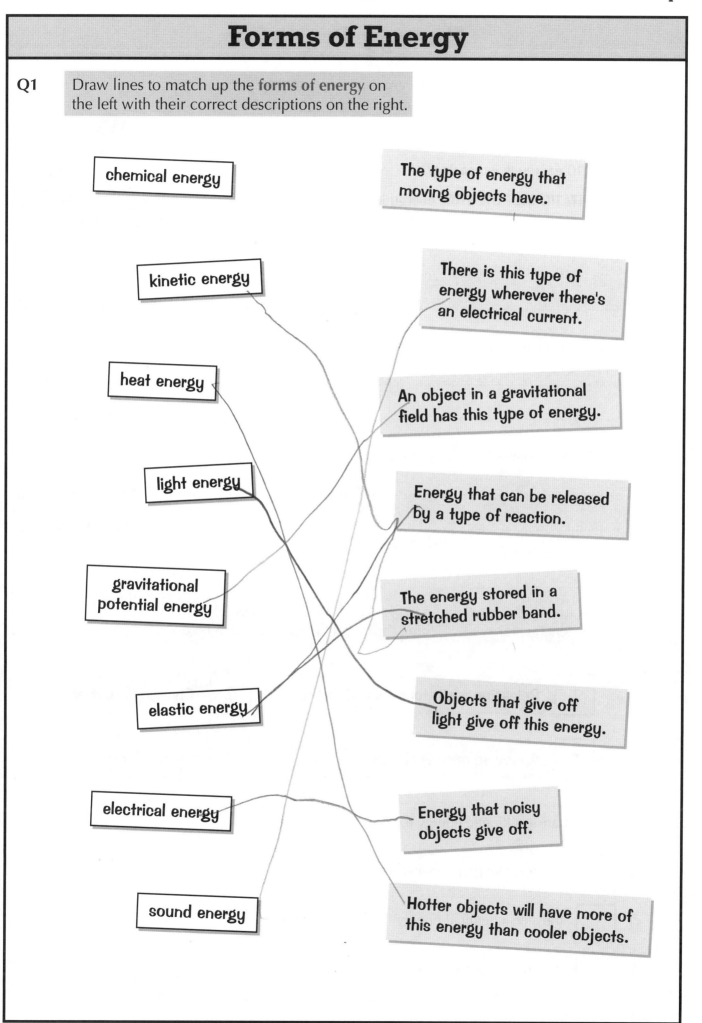

chemical energy

kinetic energy

heat energy

light energy

gravitational potential energy

elastic energy

electrical energy

sound energy

The type of energy that moving objects have.

There is this type of energy wherever there's an electrical current.

An object in a gravitational field has this type of energy.

Energy that can be released by a type of reaction.

The energy stored in a stretched rubber band.

Objects that give off light give off this energy.

Energy that noisy objects give off.

Hotter objects will have more of this energy than cooler objects.

Energy Transfer

Q1 Work out which types of energy are **increasing** and **decreasing** for each of the following energy transfers. The first one is done for you.

a) A cyclist freewheeling down a hill.

KINETIC energy is increasing.

GRAVITATIONAL POTENTIAL energy is decreasing.

b) A burning match.

.... and .... energy is increasing

.... energy is decreasing

c) An electric light bulb.

.... and .... energy is increasing

.... energy is decreasing

d) A windmill connected to a generator.

.... energy is increasing

.... energy is decreasing

Q2 The actions below are labelled **1-4**. Match up each action to the type of energy transfer by writing the correct number in each box.

| **1** | **Releasing a stretched elastic band** | | **2.** | **Charging a battery** |

| **3** | **A moving drumstick hitting a drum** | | **4** | **Driving a car** |

a) [1] transfers kinetic energy to sound energy.

b) [2] transfers electrical energy to chemical energy.

c) [4] transfers chemical energy to kinetic energy.

d) [3] transfers elastic energy to kinetic energy.

More Energy Transfer

Q1 Some types of energy can be **stored**.

a) Which of these types of energy can be stored? Circle the correct answer.

gravitational potential   sound   light   kinetic

b) What type of stored energy is transferred by burning fuels?

gravitational potential

c) How could you release the elastic energy stored in a stretched spring?

Kinet.

d) How do our bodies release the energy stored in food?

....

....

Q2 A knight pushes a boulder along flat ground. **Circle** the correct words in brackets to complete the sentences below.

The knight applies (**a force** / energy) to make the boulder move. The stored (sound / **chemical**) energy in the knight's body is transferred to (**kinetic** / elastic) energy to move the boulder.

Q3 **Complete** the following sentence about a car by picking the correct missing word(s) from the boxes below.

If a car has a **bigger force**, but transfers the **same** amount of **energy**, the distance travelled by the car will be ...... *the Larger*

the same   larger   smaller

4

Heat Transfer

Q1 Tick the boxes to show whether each of the following statements are true or false.

		True	False
a)	Heat is only transferred between objects if they are the **same** temperature.		✓
b)	When an object is heated the particles in it start to **vibrate** more.	✓	
c)	**Conduction** is when vibrating particles **pass on** energy when they bump into other particles.	✓	
d)	Only **hot** objects radiate invisible heat waves to the surroundings.		✓
e)	Objects can't absorb **radiation**.		✓
f)	Materials like cardboard and plastic transfer heat **slowly**.	✓	

Q2 Use the following words to **complete** the paragraph below.

> thermal heat temperature cooler hot

When ......*heat*...... is transferred between objects of different temperatures, it is transferred from the ......*hot*...... object to the ......*cooler*...... object. When the two objects reach ......*thermal*...... equilibrium it means they are at the same ......*temperature*.......

Q3 Scott puts an **ice cube** on a hot plate. Complete the following sentences by circling the correct word(s) in brackets.

a) Particles in the (**ice cube** / **plate**) vibrate more than the particles in the (**ice cube** / **plate**).

b) Particles in the (**ice cube** / **plate**) pass energy to particles in the (**ice cube** / **plate**).

c) The ice cube (**loses** / **gains**) energy and starts to (**cool down** / **heat up**).

d) The plate (**loses** / **gains**) energy and starts to (**cool down** / **heat up**).

Heat Transfer

Q4 Heat energy is being **transferred** between the hot and cold drinks below by heat radiation.

cold drink   hot drink

a) What is meant by heat radiation?

....

b) Which drink is absorbing more heat energy than it radiates?

cold drink

c) Which drink is getting warmer?

hot drink

Q5 Rachael is using a saucepan to heat up some soup on the cooker hob. She holds the handle of the pan, which is made of **plastic**.

tasty soup

plastic
handle

a) Circle the correct word(s) in brackets to complete each sentence.

  i) Heat is transferred from the pan to the soup because the pan is (**hotter** / **cooler**) than the soup.

  ii) Heat is transferred from the pan to Rachael's hand slowly because the plastic handle is (**an insulator** / **a capacitor**).

b) Why is it useful to have a handle that transfers heat slowly?

Because it's safer

....

6

Conservation of Energy

Q1 Fill in the blanks using the words below to make this **important law** about energy correct.

created	conserved	destroyed	transferred

Energy can never be .... nor .... ,

but is only .... from one form to another.

This means that energy is ....

Q2 A **device** usually changes energy from one form to another, allowing it to do useful work for us.

a) Do devices transfer **all** of their input energy into useful forms? ....

b) What form does the wasted energy produced by a device usually take?

....

c) Complete the following equation:

Energy INPUT = USEFUL energy + ...

Q3 Draw lines to show whether each form of energy on the left is an example of **input energy**, **useful energy** or **wasted energy** in a TV.

Heat energy

Sound energy

Electrical energy

Light energy

Useful energy

Wasted energy

Input energy

Q4 A loudspeaker transfers electrical energy to **2500 J** of useful sound energy and **500 J** of wasted heat energy. What is the total energy input? Circle the correct answer.

2000 J	500 J	3000 J	2500 J

Section 1 — Energy and Matter

Energy Resources

Q1 Fill in the gaps in the following paragraph. Use the words that are given.

| oil | die | light | fossil | gas | photosynthesis |

The Sun produces a great deal of .... energy and heat energy.

Some of this reaches the Earth. Plants can trap this energy and change it by a process

called ....

Creatures can absorb this energy by eating the plants.

When plants and animals .... they can

become buried and over millions of years they are turned into coal,

.... and ....

We call fuels formed in this way .... fuels.

Q2 Some different energy **resources** are listed below.

| natural gas | coal | waves | wind | biomass | oil |

a) Each of the energy resources listed above originally came from **one source**.
What is this 'one source'?

....

b) Which **two** energy resources above do not need photosynthesis?

.... and ....

c) Give **one** example of biomass.

....

d) Solar cells use energy supplied by the Sun.
Circle the correct words in brackets to complete the following sentence.

Solar cells convert (**light** / **kinetic**) energy into (**elastic** / **electrical**) energy.

Generating Electricity

Q1 The diagram shows a traditional electricity-generating power station.

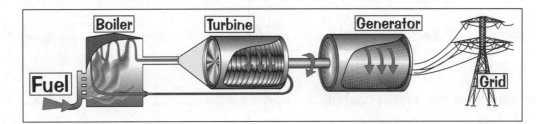

a) What type of energy is contained in the power station's fuel supply?

....

b) This energy is transferred into another form of energy in the boiler.

What type of energy is this? ....

c) What energy transfer takes place in the generator?

.... energy → .... energy

Q2 **Non-renewable** fossil fuels are often used to produce electricity for use in the home.

a) What does non-renewable mean? ....

b) Circle the correct words in brackets to complete the paragraph below.

> Fossil fuels take (**hundreds** / **millions**) of years to make, and
>
> (**a long time** / **a few minutes**) to burn. Once we've used
>
> them up, (**we can make some more** / **there will be no more**).

Q3 **Wind**, **biomass** and **waves** are examples of energy resources that make use of energy from the Sun. We know that these energy resources **won't run out**.

a) Why can we say that these energy resources won't run out?

....

....

b) What word is used to describe energy resources that won't run out?

....

The Cost of Electricity

Q1 Jane goes to a shop that sells **electrical appliances** to buy a new printer. Some information about a printer is shown below.

Inkjet-DJ

Power: 0.4 kW

Special features: Fully-functioning sound and light system

a) Circle the correct definition of an **electrical appliance**.

Anything that produces electricity.

Anything that needs electricity to work.

b) Calculate the energy transferred in kilowatt-hours by the Inkjet-DJ printer in **2 hours**.

....

....

....

c) The price per kWh is **15p**. How much will it **cost** to run the Inkjet-DJ for 2 hours?

....

....

....

Hint: Use your answer to part b) to help you.

Q2 Answer the following questions.

a) Write down the equation used to calculate energy transferred in **joules** (J).

....

b) A **700 W** blender is used for **90 seconds**. Tick the correct box to show the amount of energy transferred by the blender.

☐ 63 J   ☐ 1050 J   ☐ 63 000 J   ☐ 1.05 J

The Cost of Electricity

Q3   **Electricity meters** help you to keep track of how much electricity is being used in the home.

a)   **Circle** the units below that electricity meters usually use.

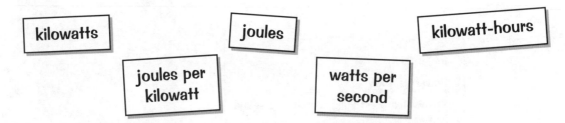

kilowatts   joules   kilowatt-hours

joules per kilowatt   watts per second

b)   Rob wants to know how much energy he uses at home in one day.
He takes an electricity meter reading at 9:00 am on Thursday and another meter reading at the same time on Friday. His meter readings look like this:

0 9 9 2 7 kWh	0 9 9 3 7 kWh
THURSDAY	**FRIDAY**

How much electrical energy was transferred in Rob's house between the readings?

....

c)   Rob's electricity company charges him **19 pence per kWh**. Calculate the cost of the electricity used in Rob's home between the meter readings.

....

....

....

d)   Rob receives an electricity bill for the electricity he has used over **30 days**.
Rob uses a similar amount of electricity every day. What should he do to the answer to part **c)** to work out how much his bill should be? Circle the correct answer.

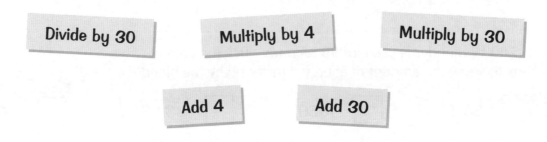

Divide by 30   Multiply by 4   Multiply by 30

Add 4   Add 30

Section 1 — Energy and Matter

Comparing Power Ratings and Energy Values

Q1   Complete the paragraph below by **circling** the correct words in brackets.

> The power rating of an appliance tells you how fast it transfers
> (**energy** / **power**). The (**higher** / **stronger**) the power rating, the
> (**higher** / **lower**) the amount of energy transferred in a given time.

Q2   The labels of some different breakfast cereals are shown below.

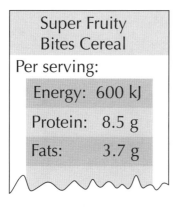

Super Fruity
Bites Cereal
Per serving:
Energy: 600 kJ
Protein: 8.5 g
Fats: 3.7 g

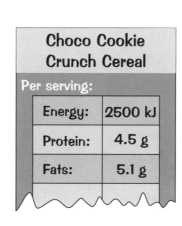

**Choco Cookie
Crunch Cereal**
Per serving:

Energy:	2500 kJ
Protein:	4.5 g
Fats:	5.1 g

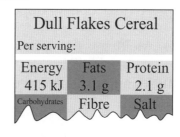

Dull Flakes Cereal
Per serving:

Energy	Fats	Protein
415 kJ	3.1 g	2.1 g
Carbohydrates	Fibre	Salt

a)   What does **kJ** stand for? ....

b)   Which cereal has the **most** energy stored in one serving?

....

Q3   Two toasters in a shop have
different **power ratings**.

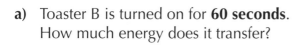

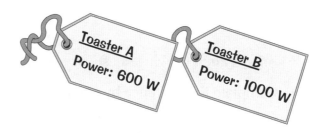

Toaster A
Power: 600 W

Toaster B
Power: 1000 W

a)   Toaster B is turned on for **60 seconds**.
How much energy does it transfer?

....

....

b)   Will toaster A transfer **more** or **less** energy than toaster B in this time? How do you know?

....

....

Physical Changes

Q1 **Complete** the sentences using the words below. You may use each word once, more than once, or not at all.

DISSOLVING CONDENSING

MELTING EVAPORATING FREEZING

a) A sugar cube 'disappearing' in a glass of water is an example of ....

b) An ice cube 'disappearing' in a glass of water is an example of ....

c) Melting is the opposite of ....

d) Windows steaming up is an example of ....

Q2 The sentences below are all describing what happens to a bucket of solid water (**ice**) when it **melts**. Place a tick next to all the sentences that are true.

☐ The mass of the water increases.   ☐ The water particles get closer together.

☐ The water becomes less dense.   ☐ The water particles are now able to flow.

☐ There is a chemical reaction.

Q3 Answer the following questions about **dissolving**.

a) Complete this sentence by circling the correct words in brackets.

> Dissolving occurs when a solid mixes with a
> (**liquid** / **solid**) to form a (**solvent** / **solution**).

b) Is dissolving an **irreversible** or **reversible** process? ....

c) A teaspoon of sugar is dissolved in a cup of tea. Does the mass of the sugar change?

....

Physical Changes

Q4 Food stored in a freezer can dry out when the **solid frozen water** in the food turns into **water vapour** (a gas).

a) What is the name of the process of a solid turning **directly** into a gas?

....

b) What happens to the **mass** of the water as it changes from a solid to a gas?

....

c) Complete the sentence below by circling the correct word in brackets.

> A solid turning into a gas is an example of a (**physical** / **chemical**) change.

d) Tick the **true** statement(s) about physical changes below.

> New substances are made during a physical change. ☐
>
> A physical change is not the same as a chemical change. ☐
>
> A physical change involves a chemical reaction. ☐

Q5 When nitrogen **gas** is cooled to temperatures below −196 °C, it forms **liquid** nitrogen.

a) What is the name of the process of a gas changing into a liquid?

....

b) What happens to the arrangement of the nitrogen particles as the gas turns to a liquid? Circle the correct answer.

They get closer together   **Nothing**   **They get further apart**

c) How will the **density** of the nitrogen change during this process?

....

d) When the liquid nitrogen starts to heat up again, it turns back into a gas. What is the name of this process?

....

Movement of Particles

Q1 The diagram below shows some smoke particles **suspended in air**.

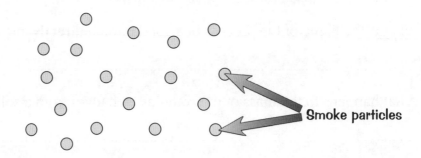

Smoke particles

a) How would you expect the smoke particles to **move** in air?
Tick one correct answer.

☐ all in one direction   ☐ randomly   ☐ in straight lines

b) What is the name of this sort of motion?

Q2 The diagram shows a box containing particles of **two gases**, gas A and gas B. The gas B particles start all in one corner of the box.

Particles of gas B

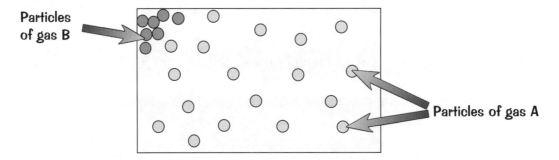

Particles of gas A

a) What would you expect to see after a long period of time?
Circle the correct picture below.

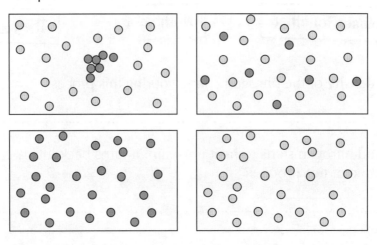

Movement of Particles

b) Complete the sentences by circling the correct words in brackets to explain part **a)**.

> All the gas particles move around at random with (**Brownian** / **Greenian**) motion.
>
> The gas B particles eventually bump their way from an area of (**high** / **low**)
>
> concentration to an area of (**high** / **low**) concentration.
>
> They will constantly bump into each other until they are (**evenly** / **unevenly**)
>
> spread out amongst the (**gas A** / **gas B**) particles.

c) What is the process described in part **b)** called? ....

Q3 Thermometers are used to measure **temperature**.
They often contain a thin glass tube with some liquid inside.

a) The following paragraph explains how a thermometer works.
Complete the sentences by filling in the blanks using the words below.

> bigger   energy   up   expand   more   increases

> As the temperature .... the liquid particles start to move around
>
> .... as they have more .... The spaces between
>
> the particles get .... , causing the liquid to ....
>
> and move .... the thin tube of the thermometer.

b) Two thermometers have been drawn below. Which thermometer shows a **high** temperature, and which shows a **low** temperature? Write the answers in boxes A and B.

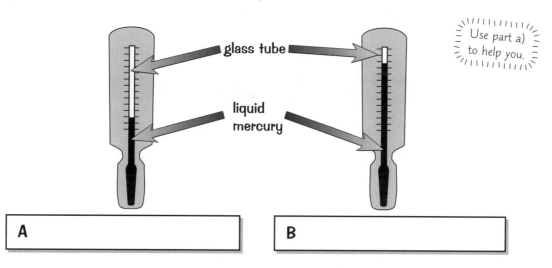

Use part a) to help you.

glass tube

liquid mercury

A

B

Speed

Q1 This question is about **speed**.

a) Complete the following sentence by filling in the blanks.

Speed is a measure of how ....

you travel in a set amount of ....

b) Which of the units below can be used to measure speed? Circle the correct units.

seconds per metre   miles per hour   metres per second

kilometres per hour   kilograms per hour

Q2 Circle the word equation below that correctly links **speed**, **distance** and **time**.

SPEED = TIME ÷ DISTANCE   SPEED = DISTANCE ÷ TIME

SPEED = TIME × DISTANCE

Q3 A car travels **12 m** in **6 seconds**. What is the **speed** of the car?

....

....

Use the equation you picked in Q2 to help you answer this question.

Q4 An aeroplane flies a distance of **700 miles**. The flight lasts **2 hours**. Calculate the **speed** of the aeroplane in mph.

....

....

Speed

Q5   Look at the distance-time graph on the right. What does the **slope** of the distance-time graph show? Circle the correct answer.

acceleration   speed

distance   time

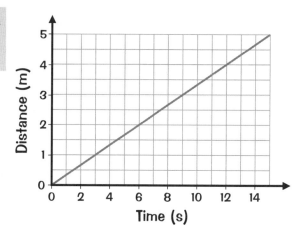

Q6   The **movement** of an object can be described using a **distance-time graph**.
A distance-time graph is shown below for the motion of a cat. For each part of the distance-time graph described below, circle what it tells you about the motion of the cat.

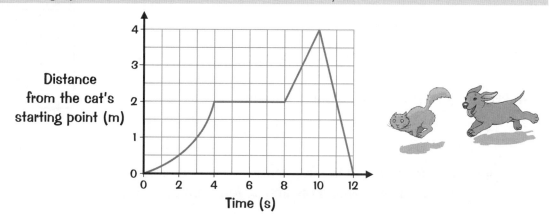

a) Between 4 and 8 seconds the distance-time graph is **flat**.

The cat is not moving   The cat is moving at a constant speed   The cat is slowing down

b) Between 8 and 10 seconds the distance-time graph is a **straight line sloping upwards**.

The cat is slowing down   The cat is moving at a constant speed   The cat is accelerating

c) Between 10 and 12 seconds the graph is a **straight line sloping downwards**.

The cat is slowing down   The cat is accelerating   The cat is travelling back towards its starting point

d) Between 0 and 4 seconds the graph is **curved**. The curve gets **steeper**.

Its speed is increasing   Its speed is decreasing   Its speed stays the same

Forces and Movement

Q1 Use the words below to **complete** these sentences.

newton meter		pulls		
	pushes		newtons	pairs

Forces are measured in .... and can be measured using

a .... They are usually .... or

.... They usually act in ....

Q2 Decide if each of the following statements are **true** or **false** and tick the correct box.

	True	False

a) Forces can't be seen.

b) The effects of forces can never be seen.

c) Objects need to touch for there to be a force between them.

d) Forces always act in a certain direction.

Q3 Draw lines to match up the five actions caused by forces on the **left** with an example of each action from the **right**.

Actions

Speed up or start moving

Change direction

Change shape

Turn

Slow down or stop moving

Examples

Unscrewing a bottle lid

Applying the brakes on a bicycle

A tennis ball bouncing off a wall

Hitting a snooker ball

Stretching an elastic band

Friction and Resistance

Q1   Circle the correct words in brackets that make the following sentences **true**.

a)   Friction is a type of (**pressure** / **force** / **momentum**).

b)   The direction that friction acts is always (**the same as** / **opposite to**) the direction of movement.

c)   To start something moving, the push or pull force must be (**bigger** / **smaller**) than resisting forces like friction.

d)   To push something out of the way, you need to (**overcome** / **produce**) friction.

e)   There will be (**friction** / **air resistance**) between two objects when their surfaces rub together.

f)   Air resistance pushes against objects moving through air to try and (**slow them down** / **speed them up**).

Q2   Sohail drops a cube into a measuring cylinder of water and times **how long** it takes to reach the **bottom**.

a)   What force causes the cube to move down through the water? ....

b)   There is a **frictional force** on the cube as it moves through the water.

i)   Name this frictional force.

    ....

ii)   In which direction does this frictional force act on the cube? Tick the box next to the correct answer.

☐ **Upwards**   ☐ **In all directions**

☐ **Downwards**   ☐ **From side to side**

Friction and Resistance

Q3 This diagram shows a sky-boarder in **free-fall** (before she opens her parachute). The arrows show the forces acting on her. **Thicker arrows** mean **bigger forces**.

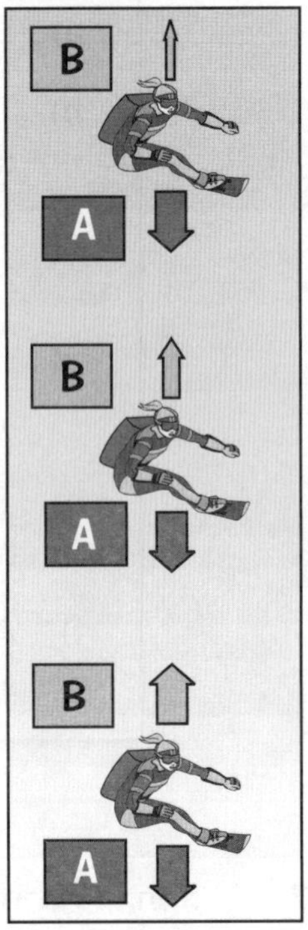

a) What is the name given to force **A**?

....

b) What is the name given to force **B**?

....

c) Complete this sentence by circling the correct word in the brackets.

Force B gets (**bigger** / **smaller**) as the sky-boarder moves faster.

d) Forces A and B on the sky-boarder are **balanced** in the last picture. Will her speed be **increasing**, **decreasing** or **constant** at this point? Circle the correct answer.

increasing   **decreasing**   **constant**

Q4 A parachutist jumps from a plane and falls through the air. The pictures on the right show the forces on the parachutist **just before** and **just after** he opens his parachute.

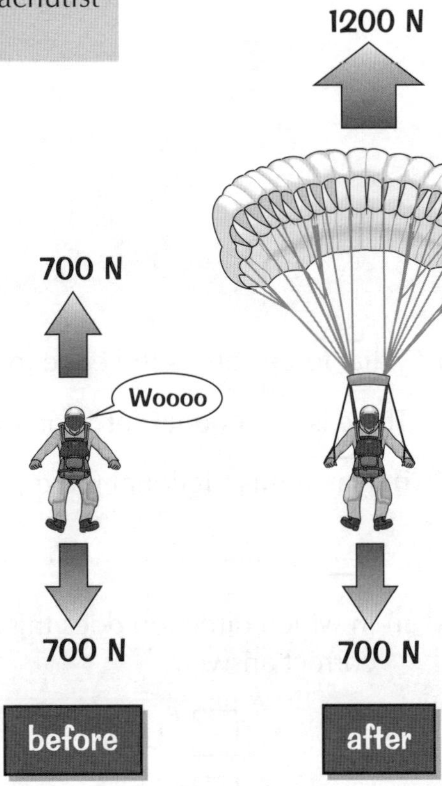

a) i) What happens to the air resistance acting on the parachutist when he opens his parachute?

....

ii) Explain why the air resistance acting on the parachutist changes in this way.

....

....

....

b) What will happen to the **speed** of the parachutist **just after** he opens the parachute?

....

1200 N

700 N

Woooo

700 N

before

700 N

after

Force Diagrams

Q1 For the sentences below, tick the correct box to show whether the forces on the object need to be **balanced** or **unbalanced**.

Balanced **Unbalanced**

a) The object remains stationary. ☐ ☐

b) The object slows down or speeds up. ☐ ☐

c) The object's direction changes. ☐ ☐

d) The object moves at the same speed in the same direction. ☐ ☐

Q2 For each of the diagrams below, say whether the forces shown are **balanced** or **unbalanced**.

200 N ← shark → 800 N

↑ 2000 N helicopter ↓ 2000 N

700 N ← car → 600 N

....

Q3 A cat has a **weight** of 35 N and is standing still on a table.

a) What direction does the weight of the cat act in?

....

b) What is the name of the other force acting on the cat?

....

c) What direction does the force named in **b)** act in?

....

d) Give the size of the force named in **b)**.

....

e) Draw **two** arrows on the diagram to show the two forces acting on the cat. Label your arrows with the **name** and **size** of the force they show.

Make sure your arrows are the right sizes.

Force Diagrams

Q4 The diagram shows the **size** and **direction** of the **forces** acting on a car. Is the car speeding up, slowing down or travelling at a constant speed? Circle the correct answer.

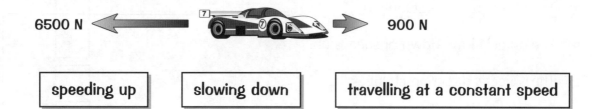

6500 N   900 N

| speeding up | slowing down | travelling at a constant speed |

Q5 In each of the following examples, work out the **overall force** and say whether the object is **slowing down**, **speeding up** or moving at a **constant speed**.

a)

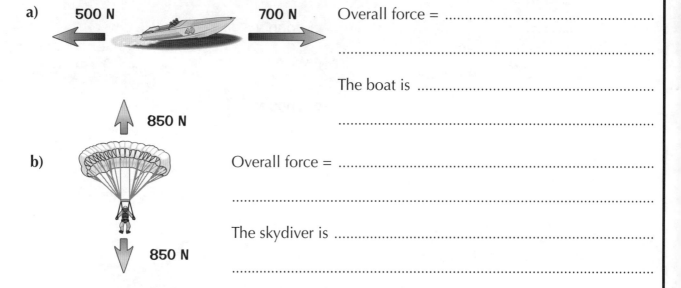

500 N   700 N

Overall force = ...

....

The boat is ....

....

b)

850 N

Overall force = ...

....

The skydiver is ....

850 N

....

Q6 A fire engine is **accelerating** due to an overall force of **20 000 N**. Its engine is applying a forward force of **22 000 N**. There is a force due to **air resistance** of **2000 N**

Complete the force diagram below by drawing a second
arrow to show the air resistance on the fire engine.
Label the arrow with the size of the force.

Engine Force

22 000 N

Moments

Q1 Forces can create **moments**.

a) Complete these sentences about moments by filling in the blanks.

i) A moment is a measure of the .... effect of a force.

ii) When a force acts on something with a ...., it can create a moment.

iii) Moments are measured in ....

b) The objects in the diagrams below **aren't moving** to start with.
Circle all the diagrams where applying the force shown will create a **moment**.

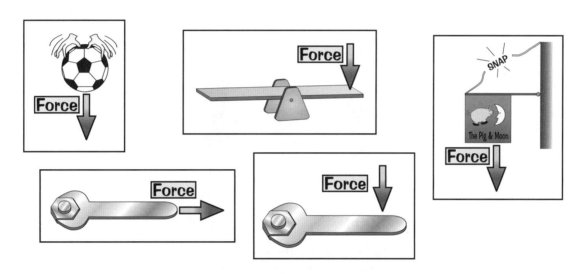

Q2 A **20 N** box is put on end of a seesaw. It is **1 m** away from the pivot of the seesaw.

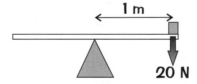

a) What is the moment caused by the box on the seesaw? Circle the correct answer.

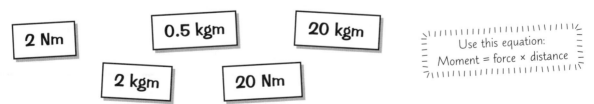

| 2 Nm | 0.5 kgm | 20 kgm |
| 2 kgm | 20 Nm | |

Use this equation:
Moment = force × distance

b) Is the moment an **anticlockwise** moment or a **clockwise** moment?

....

Moments

Q3   The moments on an object are **balanced**. Tick the box
next to the sentence below that **must** be true for the object.

☐   The anticlockwise moments must equal the clockwise moments.

☐   The forces acting on the object must all be the same size.

☐   The forces acting on the object must all be the same distance from the pivot.

Q4   Anna and Aaron sit on a seesaw. They are both **2 m from the pivot** of the seesaw.

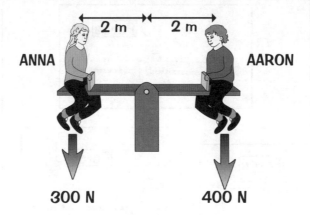

2 m   2 m

ANNA   AARON

300 N   400 N

a)   Anna has a weight of **300 N**. Complete the calculation
below to find the moment caused on the seesaw by her weight.

> Moment caused by Anna's weight = force × distance
>
> = ... N × .... m
>
> = ... Nm

b)   Aaron has a weight of **400 N**. Complete the calculation
below to find the moment caused on the seesaw by his weight.

> Moment caused by Aaron's weight = force × distance
>
> = ... N × .... m
>
> = ... Nm

c)   Complete this sentence by circling the correct words in the brackets.

> The (**clockwise** / **anticlockwise**) moment due to (**Aaron's** / **Anna's**) weight is
>
> greater than the (**clockwise** / **anticlockwise**) moment due to (**Aaron's** / **Anna's**)
>
> weight, so the seesaw moves (**clockwise** / **anticlockwise**).

Moments

Q5 The diagram shows a plank of wood **balanced** on a pivot. Use the formula in the box to help you answer the following questions.

Moment =
force × distance

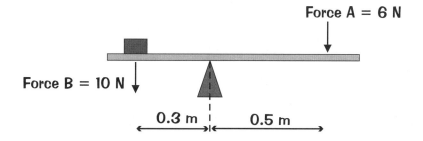

Force A = 6 N

Force B = 10 N ↓

0.3 m   0.5 m

a) Does force B create a **clockwise** or an **anticlockwise** moment?

....

b) Use the formula to calculate the size of the **moment** created by force B.

....

....

c) The moments are **balanced**.
What must the size of the moment created by force A be?

....

Q6 The diagram below shows a dog and a squirrel on a seesaw.
The anticlockwise and clockwise moments on the seesaw are **balanced**.

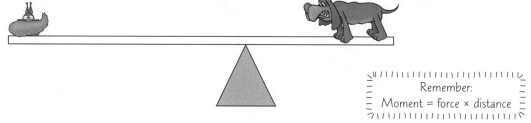

Remember:
Moment = force × distance

The dog moves **towards** the squirrel. Tick the sentence(s) that are true below.

☐ The moments created by the dog and the squirrel are no longer balanced.

☐ The moment created by the dog has decreased.

☐ The seesaw will rotate anticlockwise.

☐ The seesaw will rotate clockwise.

Forces and Elasticity

Q1   A rubber band is an **elastic** object that can be **deformed**.

   a) i) What is meant by **deforming** an object?

   ....

   ii) What needs to be applied to an object to deform it?

   ....

   b) What is an **elastic** object? Tick the box next to the correct answer.

   ☐   Any object that can be stretched or compressed

   ☐   Any object that can be stretched or compressed easily

   ☐   Any object that can be stretched or compressed and return to its original shape

   c) Give another example of an elastic object.

   ....

Q2   Dennis has made a slingshot from a length of **elastic** and a piece of wood. He uses it to fire pebbles at a target. **Complete** the following sentences using the words in the boxes.

shape   stretching   kinetic

stored elastic   deforms

work

Dennis .... the elastic by .... it.

He is doing .... by transferring ....

energy into .... energy in the elastic.

When he releases the elastic, it returns to its original ....

Forces and Elasticity

Q3   Springs obey **Hooke's Law**. Circle the correct words in the
brackets to complete these sentences about Hooke's Law.

a)   Hooke's Law says that as you increase the force on an object to stretch it, the amount the
object is stretched (**increases** / **decreases**) at (**double the** / **half the** / **the same**) rate.

b)   Hooke's Law only applies (**up to** / **over**) a certain force.

c)   The force at which Hooke's Law stops working for springs is
(**higher** / **lower**) than for most other materials.

d)   The force and extension of a spring obeying Hooke's Law are
(**directly** / **inversely**) proportional.

Q4   Antonio is hanging a series of weights from the
end of a spring, as shown in the diagram below.

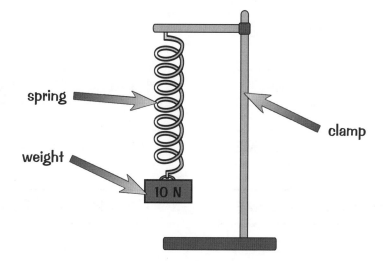

a)   He hangs a **10 N** weight on the spring. The spring holds the weight still.
What is the **size** of the force exerted by the spring on the weight?

....

b)   What **direction** is the force exerted by the spring on the weight acting in?

....

c)   Complete the following sentence to describe the forces on the spring.

The forces on the spring are in ....

Pressure

Q1 This question is about **pressure**.

a) What is pressure a measure of? Circle the correct answer.

The force over a certain volume

The force over a certain area

The mass over a certain force

The area over a certain force

b) Complete the sentence below by circling the correct words in brackets.

The more (**force** / **mass** / **area**) there is over a given

(**area** / **force** / **mass** / **volume**), the (**greater** / **smaller**) the pressure.

Q2 Circle the correct equation for pressure below.

PRESSURE = FORCE × AREA

PRESSURE = MASS ÷ AREA

PRESSURE = FORCE ÷ VOLUME

PRESSURE = MASS × VOLUME

PRESSURE = FORCE × VOLUME

PRESSURE = FORCE ÷ AREA

Q3 Pressure can be measured using different **units**.

Complete the following sentence about units of pressure using the words in the box.

N   area   pressure   Pa

If a force of 1 .... is spread over an ....
of 1 m², then it exerts a .... of 1 ....

Pressure

Q4 What is 75 N/m² in **pascals** (Pa)? Circle the correct answer.

7.5 Pa   750 Pa   75 Pa   0.75 Pa

Q5 What is **0.6 Pa** in **newtons per metre squared** (N/m²)? Circle the correct answer.

6 N/m²   0.6 N/m²   60 N/m²   600 N/m²

Q6 Each of the boxes shown below weighs **20 N**.

a) What is the size of the force that each box applies to the ground?

....

b) Which box applies the **least pressure** to the floor? Circle the correct answer.

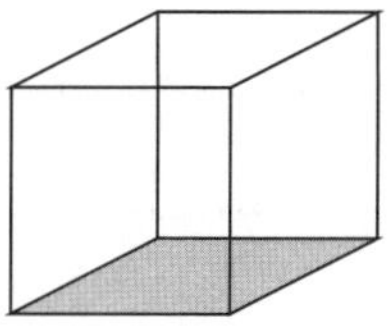

Base area 6 m²   Base area 12 m²   Base area 18 m²

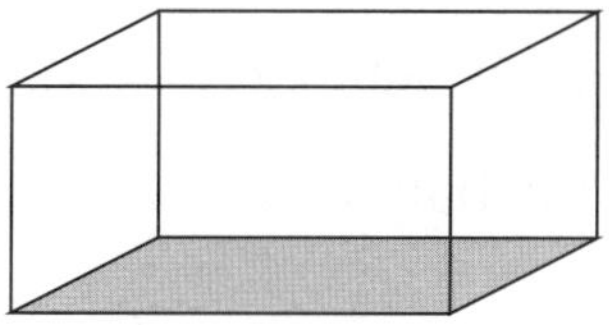

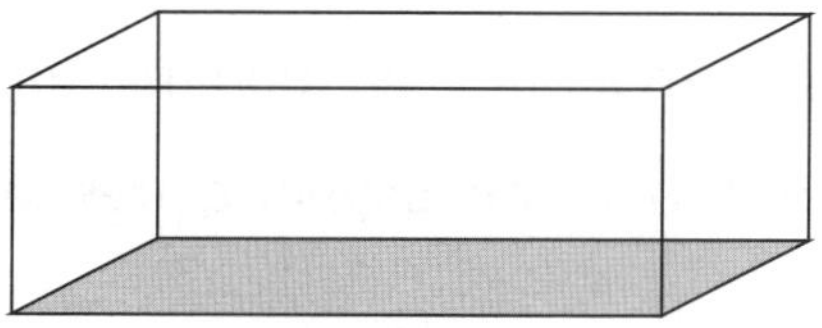

Q7 Alice wants to find the **pressure** applied by an elephant standing on the floor. The area of each of the elephant's feet is **0.25 m²**. The weight of the elephant is spread over the elephant's **four** feet.

a) Calculate the **total area** the weight of the elephant is spread over.

....

b) The weight of the elephant is **30 000 N**. What pressure will the elephant apply to the floor? Tick the box next to the correct answer.

☐ 120 000 N/m²   ☐ 60 000 N/m²

☐ 30 000 N/m²   ☐ 15 000 N/m²

Pressure

Q8 A hot air balloon takes off from a field. It rises **upwards** for a while, before travelling **back down** to land again. Use the words below to complete the following sentences.

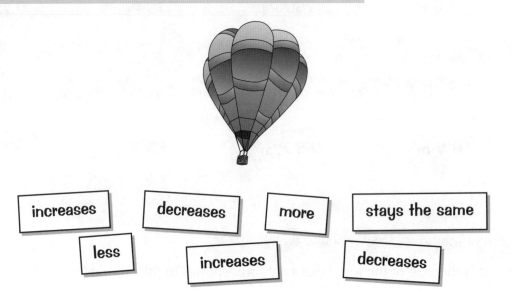

| increases | decreases | more | stays the same |

| less | increases | decreases |

As the balloon gets **higher** there is .... atmosphere above it

so the **weight** of the atmosphere pressing down on it ....

The **area** of the balloon that this weight is acting on ....

and so the **atmospheric pressure** on the balloon ....

When the balloon **loses height** there is .... atmosphere above

it. The **weight** of the atmosphere pressing down on it ....

and so the **atmospheric pressure** on the balloon ....

Q9 Tick the correct box to show whether each sentence below is **true** or **false**.

True False

a) The higher you go in the atmosphere, the lower the pressure.

b) The pressure in liquids increases with depth.

c) The pressure at the bottom of the ocean is less than at the top of the ocean.

d) If you place an object in water, it will experience water pressure from all directions.

Pressure

Q10   The picture shows a submarine in the ocean.

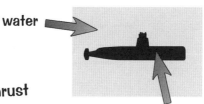
water

submarine

a) What is the name of the **force** caused by water pressure that acts upwards on the submarine? Circle the correct answer.

weight   air resistance   friction   upthrust

b) Complete these sentences about the force on the submarine by circling the correct words in the brackets.

> The force caused by water pressure pushing upwards at the bottom of the submarine is (**bigger than** / **smaller than** / **the same as**) the force caused by water pressure pushing down at the top of the submarine.

Q11   For each of the objects below, look at the weight and upthrust and decide whether they will **sink** or **float** in water.

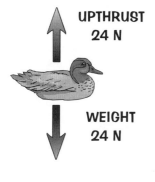
UPTHRUST
24 N

WEIGHT
24 N

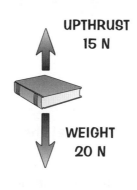
UPTHRUST
15 N

WEIGHT
20 N

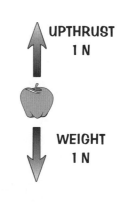
UPTHRUST
1 N

WEIGHT
1 N

....

Q12   The diagram below shows someone pushing a drawing pin. In **case 1**, they press down on the **flattened end** of the pin to push it into a board. In **case 2**, they push down with the **same force** on the **sharp end** of the pin, but it does not go into the board.

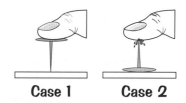
Case 1   Case 2

Use pressure and area to explain why can you push the drawing pin into a board in case 1, but not in case 2.

....

....

....

....

Water Waves

Q1   The diagram shows a **water wave** in a bath tub.

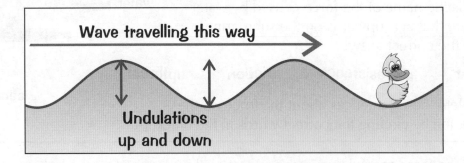

a)   Complete the sentence below by circling the correct answers in the brackets.

> Water waves are a type of (**transverse** / **longitudinal**) wave. The undulations
>
> of the water wave are (**at right-angles to** / **in the same direction as**) the
>
> direction that the wave is travelling in.

b) i) What does the water wave transfer?

....

ii) Which direction does your answer to **b) i)** get transferred in? Tick the correct answer(s).

☐ **In the same direction that the wave is travelling in.**

☐ **In the same direction as the undulations of the wave.**

c)   What will happen to the wave when it hits the side of the bath tub?

....

d)   Filling in the missing labels on the diagram of a water wave below.

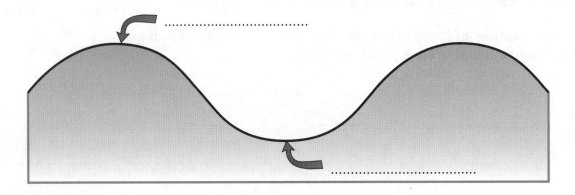

Water Waves

Q2 Some students are looking at what happens when two waves **meet** in the middle of a tank of water.

a) i) The two **crests** shown below meet in the middle of the tank.

Circle the diagram that shows what happens when the two waves meet.

A B C

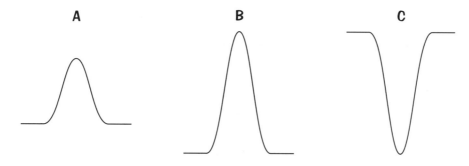

ii) The two **troughs** shown below meet in the middle of the tank.

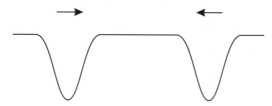

Circle the diagram that shows what happens when the two waves meet.

A B C

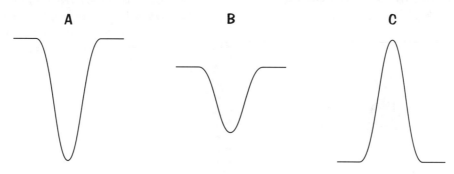

b) Describe what would happen if a **crest** with a height of **3 cm** met a **trough** with a depth of **3 cm** in the middle of the tank.

The depth of the trough and the height of the crest are exactly the same.

....

....

Light Waves

Q1   This question is about **luminous objects**.

a) What is a **luminous** object?

....

....

b) Circle all of the examples below that are luminous objects.

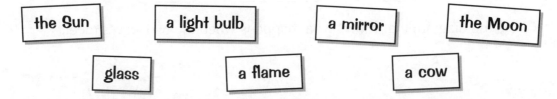

the Sun   a light bulb   a mirror   the Moon

glass   a flame   a cow

Q2   This question is about how light helps us to **see**.

a) Complete the following sentences by circling the correct words in brackets.

> Light always travels in a (**straight** / **curved**) line. We can
>
> see because light produced by (**shiny** / **luminous**) objects is
>
> (**deflected** / **reflected**) off other objects and into our (**ears** / **eyes**).

b) Complete the **path** of the light in the diagram below to show how light from the bulb reaches the eye.

Use a ruler to complete the path. The light ray should go to the pupil (the black bit) of the eye. Draw an arrow on your line to show the direction the light is going.

Bulb

Wall

Eye

Mirror

Light Waves

Q3 Tick the correct box to show whether the sentences are true for **water waves** only, **light waves** only or **both**.

	Water only	Light only	Both
a) These waves are **transverse** waves.	☐	☐	☐
b) These waves can be **reflected**.	☐	☐	☐
c) These waves transfer **energy** from one place to another.	☐	☐	☐
d) These waves always travel at the **same speed** in space.	☐	☐	☐
e) The undulations in these waves are at **right angles** to the direction the wave is travelling in.	☐	☐	☐

Q4 The space between the Earth and the Sun is mostly a **vacuum**.

Not this kind of vacuum.

a) Complete these sentences by circling the correct words in brackets.

> Light waves (**need** / **don't need**) particles to travel, but water waves (**do** / **don't**). There (**are** / **aren't any**) particles in a vacuum, so water waves (**can** / **can't**) travel though them, but light waves (**can** / **can't**).

b) i) In which of the following will light travel **fastest**? Tick the correct option.

Air ☐   Water ☐   Vacuum ☐

ii) Complete this sentence using one of the phrases below to fill in the gap.

stopped by   **slowed down by**   **sped up by**

> Light waves are .... particles.

c) What is the **speed** of light in a vacuum?

....

Remember to include the right unit for the speed in your answer.

Reflection

Q1 Look at the **diagram** to the right.

light rays   object

a) What happens to the light when it hits the object?

....

....

b) Tick a box for each sentence to show which
sentences are **true** and which are **false**.

	True	False
Light is only reflected off mirrors.	☐	☐
Light is not reflected off objects with a rough surface.	☐	☐
Light is only reflected off objects with a shiny surface.	☐	☐
Light is reflected off most objects.	☐	☐

Q2 Mirrors appear shiny because of **reflection**.

a) Complete this paragraph using some of the words in the box below.

smooth   reflected   same   different   specular   refracted

Mirrors have a very .... shiny surface. When light

hits a mirror at an angle, all the light is .... at the

.... angle, giving a clear reflection. This is known as

.... reflection.

b) i) Describe how light reflects off **rough** surfaces like paper.

....

....

ii) Circle the name of this kind of reflection.

medium scattering   opaque scattering

specular scattering   diffuse scattering

Reflection

Q3   This question is about **reflection**.

a) What is the **law of reflection**?

....

b) Follow these instructions to draw a **ray diagram** for light reflecting off the mirror in the box below:

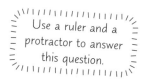
Use a ruler and a protractor to answer this question.

- Draw a ray of light hitting the mirror where the normal meets the mirror. The angle between the ray and the normal should be 50° (50 degrees).

- Add an arrow to the ray to show its direction.

- Label the angle of incidence and write what its value is.

- Draw in the reflected ray, making sure the angle is right.

- Add an arrow to the reflected ray to show its direction.

- Label the angle of reflection and write what its value is.

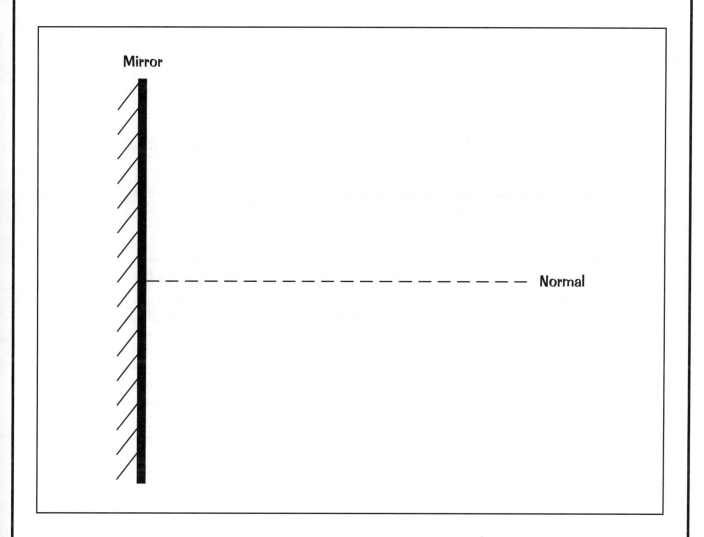

Refraction

Q1   This question is about light passing through a **medium**.

a) What is a medium?

....

....

b) Complete these sentences by circling the correct words in the brackets:

> When light moves from one medium into another, its speed
>
> (**isn't** / **is**) changed. If the light enters the new medium at an angle,
>
> it (**bends** / **continues in the same direction**). This happens because
>
> the speed of light is (**the same** / **different**) in different materials.
>
> The name given to this effect is (**reflection** / **deflection** / **refraction**).

Q2   Objects can be **transparent** or **opaque**.

a) Write **transparent** and **opaque** next to their correct definition below.

Light can't travel through these objects.   ....

Light can travel through these objects.   ....

b) Write a **T** in the boxes next to all the objects below that are **transparent**,
and write an **O** in the boxes next to all the objects below that are **opaque**.

☐ jam jar	☐ window	☐ wall
☐ brick	☐ wine glass	☐ water
☐ sheep	☐ tree	☐ glasses lens

Refraction

Q3 The diagrams below show a ray of light travelling through a **glass** block.

a) Diagram **A** is correct. Which other diagram, **B**, **C** or **D**, below is correct?

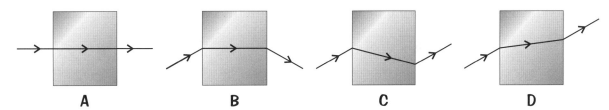

A	B	C	D

Answer = ...

b) Why does the light ray shown in diagram A **not** change direction? Tick the correct reason.

☐ The light ray's speed doesn't change.   ☐ Light travels in straight lines.

☐ The light ray hits the glass straight on.   ☐ The glass is transparent.

Q4 Complete these statements by writing either **towards** or **away from** in each blank space.

When light travels from a more dense medium to a less dense medium, the light rays bend .... the normal.

When light travels from a less dense medium to a more dense medium, the light rays bend .... the normal.

Q5 The sketch below shows a ray of light travelling from **air** into **glass**.
The light ray changes direction as it goes into the glass.
Complete the sketch to show the path of the light ray in the glass.

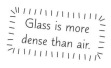

Glass is more dense than air.

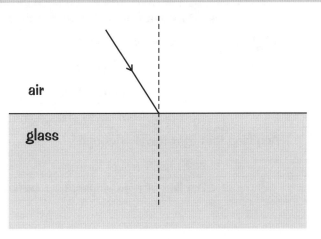

air

glass

Refraction

Q6   A diver shines a torch upwards from under the surface of the water.

> Water is more dense than air.

a)   Look at diagrams **A** and **B** below.
Which of them shows the light rays bending in the correct direction? ....

A

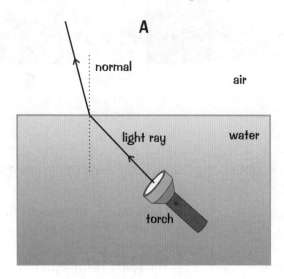

B

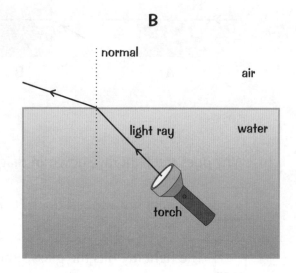

b)   Complete the sentence using one of the phrases below.

speeds up	slows down

The light ray from the torch .... when it leaves the water.

Q7   Find the missing words and write them in the grid.

	R						Light will travel through _____ materials		
	E				Refraction occurs when light enters a more or less _____ material				
	F			When it moves from one material to another light can _____					
	R		A light wave is also known as a light _____						
	A		Going from glass to air, light bends _____ from the normal.						
	C		There's no refraction if the _____ ray is at 90° to the glass						
	T		Going from air to glass, light bends _____ the normal						
	I	Anything that light travels through							
	O		Light can't travel through _____ materials						
	N	The line at right-angles to a surface							

Lenses and Cameras

Q1 Miranda used a **pinhole camera** to look at an eagle.

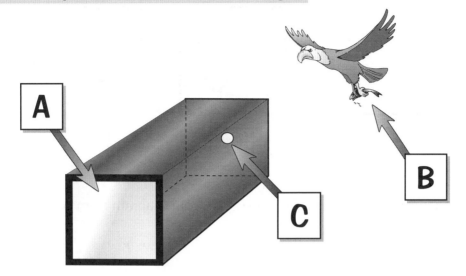

a) Draw lines to match up each letter from the diagram to the correct label.

A
B
C

The object being viewed

Pinhole

Tracing paper

b) Circle the **correct** words in the brackets to complete these sentences.

Light travels in (**straight** / **curved**) lines from the object being viewed

through the (**tracing paper** / **pinhole**) towards the (**tracing paper** / **pinhole**).

The pinhole is very (**large** / **small**), so only one (**ray** / **image**) from

each point on the object gets into the camera.

c) Draw **one more** ray of light on the diagram of a pinhole camera below
to show how the light from the exciting looking stick gets to the tracing paper.

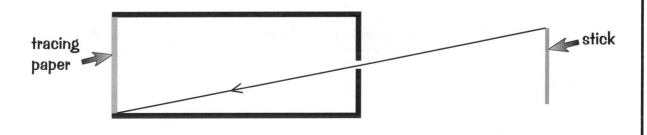

tracing paper   stick

Lenses and Cameras

d) **i)** Put a tick (✔) in the box below the image she would see on the tracing paper.

☐ ☐ ☐

ii) Why does the image appear like this? Use your diagram from part **c)** to help you.

....

....

Q2 These boxes explain how we see objects on **sunny days**. Put them in the correct order by writing the numbers **1-4** next to each box.

Light is focused
further by the lens.   ☐

                                          The cornea of each eye focuses
                                          most of the incoming light.   ☐

Light from the Sun is reflected
by objects towards our eyes.   ☐

                                          An image is formed
                                          on the retina.   ☐

Q3 Complete the sentence about the human eye by using the correct word(s) below.

upside down   upright   blurry   black and white

An image formed on the eye's retina will be ....
because the light rays cross over.

Lenses and Cameras

Q4 The **human eye** is made up of many different parts.

a) Write down the name of the part of the eye being described using the words below.

cornea	lens	retina

   i) The cells here are **photo-sensitive**. ....

   ii) A **convex** transparent 'window' that does most of the eye's focussing. ....

   iii) Another part of the eye that helps to **focus light**. ....

b) Use the words in part **a)** to label the diagram below.

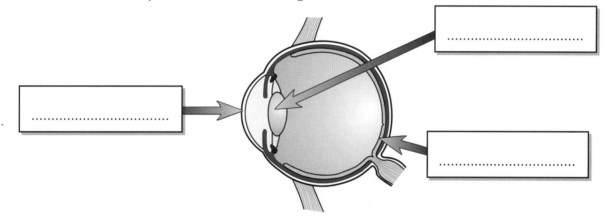

Q5 **Convex lenses** focus light rays by bending them.

a) What is the name of this bending effect?

....

b) Complete the diagram below showing how a **convex lens** focuses these three rays of light.

Use a ruler to draw straight lines. Don't forget to add arrows too.

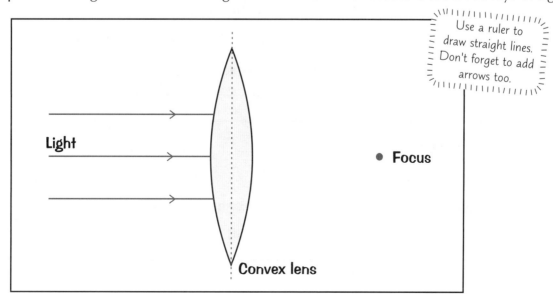

Light

• Focus

Convex lens

Lenses and Cameras

Q6   Sources of light emit **energy**, which is carried by the light waves until they hit an **absorber**.

a)   What is an absorber? ....

....

b)   What is transferred when light hits an absorber? ....

c)   Place a tick next to any objects below that are examples of absorbers.

☐   Light bulb   ☐   Film in a film camera

☐   Retina cell in the eye   ☐   The Sun

☐   Candle   ☐   Sensor in a digital camera

Q7   Use the words in boxes to complete the sentences below correctly.
You may use each word once, more than once or not at all.

retina	light	electrical	lamp	computer
brain	energy	lens	chemical	sensor

> When light enters the eye, ... is transferred to the
>
> eye's .... by the light, causing ....
>
> and .... changes in cells at the back of the eye.
>
> These changes cause signals to be sent to the ....

> When light enters a digital camera, ... is
>
> transferred to the camera's .... by the light, causing
>
> it to produce an .... charge. Changes in charge
>
> are read by a .... and turned into a digital image.

Light and Colour

Q1   Complete these sentences by circling the **correct** answer in the brackets.

a) Light from the Sun and light bulbs is often called (**coloured** / **white**) light.

b) Light can be split into its colours using a (**mirror** / **prism**).

c) This splitting is called (**deflection** / **reflection** / **dispersal**).

d) The pattern of colours made like this is called a (**spectrum** / **spectre** / **pigment**).

Q2   Light from a torch is passed through a glass prism. It **splits** into different colours, as shown in the diagram below.

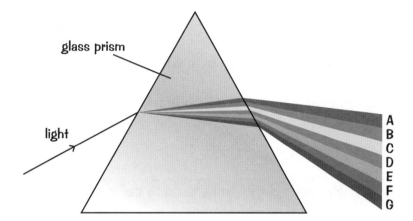

a) **i)** Name the colour that is bent the **most** by the prism. ....

      ii) Using your answer to part **a) i)**, fill in the names of each
          colour on the diagram in the spaces below.

A ....   B ....   C ....   D ....

E ....   F ....   G ....

b) Fill in the gaps to make the sentences correct using some of the following words.

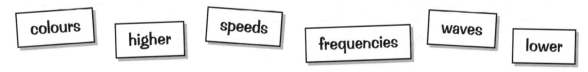

    i) Different colours are caused by light waves having different ....

    ii) Red light has a .... frequency than violet light.

    iii) The number of .... of light that pass a
         point per second is called the frequency.

Absorption and Reflection of Colour

Q1   Coloured objects interact with white light in different ways.

a)   Use the words in the box to fill in the gaps in the sentences below.

REFLECTS	YELLOW	ALL	ABSORBS

A post box is red because the paint on it .... red light and

.... all the other colours. A dandelion flower appears yellow because

it absorbs .... the colours of light except for ....

b)   Answer the following questions by
placing a tick in the correct box.

	All colours	No colours
i) Which colours of light are reflected by a **white** object?	☐	☐
ii) Which colours of light are absorbed by a **black** object?	☐	☐

Q2   Pieces of coloured plastic or glass can be used as **colour filters**.

a)   **i)** What colour(s) of light does a **red** filter let through? ....

  ii) What happens to the colour(s) that aren't let through the red filter?

  ....

b)   The diagram shows white light being shone at a **green** filter.
Write a colour in each box so that the diagram is fully labelled.

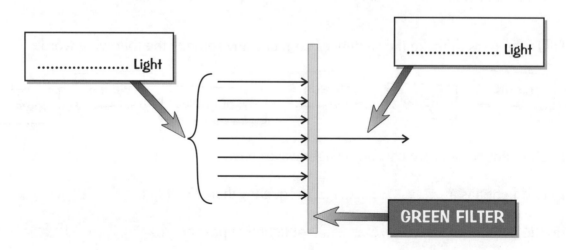

.... Light

.... Light

GREEN FILTER

Absorption and Reflection of Colour

Q3 Mick is looking at coloured plastic cubes in different colours of light.

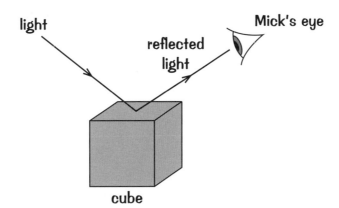

light

reflected
light

Mick's eye

cube

a) **i)** Mick shines **white** light on a **red** cube.
Complete the following sentence by filling in the gaps with the words below.

red   not red

The cube will absorb the light that is ....

and reflect the light that is ....

ii) What colour will the cube appear? ....

b) **i)** Mick shines **green** light on the same **red** cube. What colour will the cube appear?

....

ii) Circle the correct reason for your answer to **b) i)**.

The cube only
reflects black light.

The cube absorbs
all the green light so
no light is reflected.

The light is not
bright enough.

c) What colour will a **green** cube appear under **green** light? Circle the correct colour.

white   black   green

Absorption and Reflection of Colour

Q4 Most **street lights** give out mainly **orange** light.

a) Complete the following sentences using each of the words below **once**.

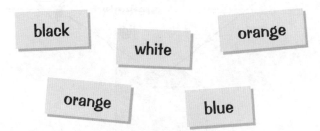

> At night, the only light on the street is orange. An ....
>
> car or a .... car would reflect all of the orange light, so
>
> it would appear .... A .... car would
>
> absorb all of the orange light, so it would appear ....

b) Street lights are gradually being changed so that they give out **white light**. Match up each of these car colours with the colour they will appear on a street lit by white light.

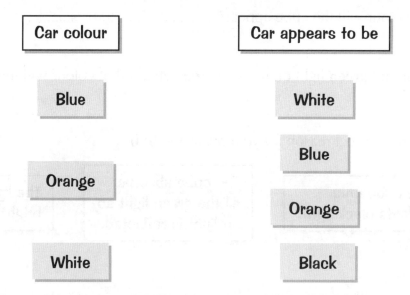

c) Circle the correct word(s) in brackets to complete the sentence below.

> (**White** / **Orange**) light is better than (**white** / **orange**)
>
> light for street lights because everything appears
>
> (**its actual colour** / **a different colour**) in white light.

Sound

Q1   Decide if each of the following sentences is **true** or **false**. Put a tick in the correct box for each one.

	True	False
a) Sound waves are caused by **vibrating** objects.	☐	☐
b) Sound travels as a **transverse** wave.	☐	☐
c) Sound can be **refracted**.	☐	☐

Q2   This question is about longitudinal waves.

a)   Complete these sentences by writing the word **parallel** or **perpendicular** in each gap.

i)   The vibrations in longitudinal waves are .... to the direction of travel of the wave.

ii)   The vibrations in longitudinal waves are .... to the direction of energy transfer.

b)   Circle the example(s) of longitudinal waves below.

water waves	light waves	sound waves	waves on a slinky pushed at the end

Q3   Sylvia stood a ringing alarm clock on top of a block of **foam** inside a bell jar. When the **air** was removed from the bell jar with a **pump**, the ringing sound **stopped**.

a)   The ringing **stopped** because sound waves couldn't travel in the jar once the air was removed. Explain why.

....

....

....

....

Think about whether there are particles inside the jar.

b)   The foam block **absorbed** the sound vibrations and stopped them reaching the base of the jar.

i) What makes foam good at absorbing sound? ....

ii) Name **two** other things which are good at absorbing sound.

.... and ....

Sound

Q4 Use the correct words below to complete the sentences in the box about **sound**.

compressions	mediums	vibrations

Sounds travel through .... When something

vibrates, it passes on the sound .... to the particles

next to it. These vibrations are then passed through the medium as a

series of .... — areas of squashed-up particles.

Q5 Russell is standing on a cliff, when a huge **explosion** is set off in the quarry below.

a) **i)** Which type of wave travels **faster**?
Circle the correct answer.

Light	Sound

ii) Complete the following sentence by circling the correct word in brackets.

Russell (**saw** / **heard**) the explosion before he (**saw** / **heard**) it.

b) Sound waves reach Russell through the **ground** and through the **air**.
Which ones will travel faster?

....

c) Russell also heard an **echo** of the sound of the explosion.
What causes an echo?

....

....

Hearing

Q1 This question is about **frequency** of sound. Complete the sentences by circling the correct word in the brackets.

a) Frequency is the number of (**waves** / **sounds**) per second.

b) Frequency is a measure of (**pitch** / **hertz**).

c) A (**high** / **low**) frequency means a high-pitched sound.

d) Frequency is measured in (**pitch** / **hertz**).

Q2 The parts of the **ear** have been labelled A-E in the diagram below.

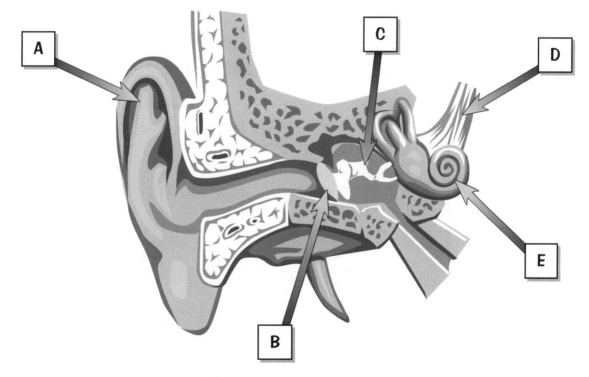

Match up each letter with the correct name for that part.

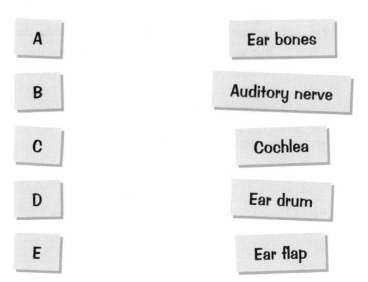

Hearing

Q3 A sound machine can produce different **frequencies** of sound.
Some of these frequencies are written below.

100 000 Hz   25 Hz   2500 Hz   500 Hz   50 000 Hz

a) Which of these frequencies has the **highest pitch**? ....

b) Which of these frequencies has the **lowest pitch**? ....

Q4 Different species of animal can hear different ranges of **frequencies**.
The **ranges** for some animals are shown on the graph below.

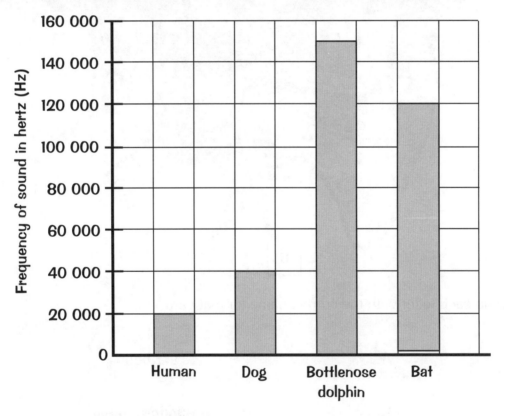

a) Use the **graph** above to find the answers to these questions.

i) What's the highest frequency that a **dog** can hear? .... Hz

ii) Which animal can hear the **highest-pitched** sounds? ....

iii) Which animal can hear the **widest range** of frequencies? ....

Hearing

b) i) The **lowest** frequency of sound that humans can hear is about **20 Hz**.
Using the graph on the previous page, write down the auditory range of humans.

.... Hz to .... Hz

ii) Using your answer to part **b) i)**, circle any sound that a **human** could hear.

Elephants calling to
each other (13 Hz)

A meteor burning up in
the atmosphere (4 Hz)

A person talking
(500 Hz)

A dog whistle
(23 000 Hz)

The bottom string on
a guitar (330 Hz)

Bats hunting insects
(120 000 Hz)

Q5 Each sentence below is a stage in the process of a person hearing a drumbeat.
Write the numbers **1 – 7** next to each sentence to put them in the correct order.

The vibrations of the drum surface
are passed to the air particles.

The ear drum vibrates.

A message is sent to the brain.

The ear bones vibrate.

The air particles vibrate.

The surface of the drum vibrates.

Hairs in the cochlea vibrate.

Energy and Waves

Q1 Use the correct words in the box to complete this paragraph about **waves**.

| information | particles | waves | recording | vibrations |

When .... transfer energy from one place to another,

they can also transfer .... Sound waves do this

through .... between ....

This is useful for .... and replaying sounds.

Q2 A news reporter is using a **microphone** to **record** a news story that will be broadcast later on.

In other news, aliens invaded Norwich today.

a) The microphone contains a **diaphragm**.
Name **two** things the diaphragm could be made from.

1 — ....

2 — ....

b) Humans talk by vibrating their vocal chords. How do
the **vibrations** of the reporter's vocal chords **travel** to the microphone?

....

c) Complete the following sentences by circling the correct word(s) in brackets.

The (**frequencies** / **vibrations**) in a sound wave make the

(**vocal chords** / **diaphragm**) vibrate inside the microphone.

The microphone turns the vibrations into (**sounds** / **electrical signals**).

d) The electrical signals are **recorded** in a computer. Which **device** could be used to
turn the electrical signals back into **sound waves**? Circle the correct answer.

| keyboard | microphone | loudspeaker | vocal chords |

Energy and Waves

Q3 Milena is listening to some music on her **computer**. Write letters in the spaces below, in the correct order, to explain how the computer produces the **sound waves**. The first letter has been done for you.

A | This makes air vibrate, producing sound waves.

B | Electrical signals are sent to the computer speakers.

C | Sound waves are sent to the computer speakers.

D | The sound waves make the diaphragm vibrate.

E | The electrical signals make the diaphragm vibrate.

F | This makes the air vibrate, producing light waves.

.... **B** .... ➡ .... ➡ ....

Q4 **Ultrasound** is a type of sound wave. Complete the following sentences about ultrasound by circling the correct word(s) in brackets.

Ultrasound is (**high** / **low**) frequency sound that is outside the normal auditory range of humans. Humans (**can** / **can't**) hear ultrasound (**at all** / **loudly**).

Q5 Dirty objects can sometimes be cleaned with **ultrasonic cleaning**.

Ultrasonic just means it uses ultrasound waves.

a) Complete the sentence using some of the words below.

clean   vibrations   waves   dirty

.... from the ultrasound ....
remove dirt from the object, leaving it ....

b) Give **two** examples of objects that can be cleaned with ultrasound waves.

1. ....

2. ....

Energy and Waves

Q6 Some physiotherapists think that **ultrasound** waves can treat pains in muscles. However, scientists **haven't** found any **evidence** that this actually works.

a) Explain why physiotherapists think that ultrasound waves can treat pain **inside** the body.

....

....

b) A scientist wants to do an **experiment** to find out if ultrasound physiotherapy can heal pain. He finds **two people** with muscle pain. He gives one **ultrasound physiotherapy**, and the other **no treatment** at all.

i) Tick (✔) all the things the scientist should do to make sure his test is **fair**.

☐ Give ultrasound physiotherapy to both people.

☐ Make sure the people are about the same age.

☐ Make sure both people have pain in the same muscle.

☐ Tell the people that he doesn't think the treatment will work.

ii) Both people took the **same** amount of time to get better. Tick the best **conclusion** for this experiment.

☐ **Ultrasound physiotherapy made muscle pain heal faster**

☐ **Ultrasound physiotherapy didn't have any effect on muscle pain**

☐ **Ultrasound physiotherapy made muscle pain worse**

A conclusion is just a summary of what the results of your experiment showed.

iii) Circle **two** ways the scientist could **improve** the experiment from the options below.

Use a bigger sample.

Test people without muscle pain.

Only test one person with muscle pain.

Repeat the experiment.

Electrical Circuits

Q1   Write down whether you think each sentence is **true** or **false**.

a)   Current can still flow when a circuit is broken. ....

b)   The moving charges in a circuit are negative electrons. ....

c)   Potential difference is the size of the current through a circuit. ....

Q2   Circle the circuit(s) below in which the bulb will be lit.

The bulb will light if a current flows through the circuit.

Q3   **Electric current** flows through circuits.

a)   What is electric current?

....

....

b)   Circle the correct word(s) in the brackets to complete this sentence.

The current in a circuit (**gets** / **does not get**) used up as it flows round the circuit.

Q4   Batteries provide the **driving force** to push charge around a circuit.

a)   What is this driving force called?

....

b)   What happens to the **current** in a circuit if you increase this driving force?
Circle the correct answer.

| The current will decrease | The current will increase | The current will stay the same |

Electrical Circuits

Q5   Electricity can't pass easily through wood because it has a high **resistance**.

a) What effect does resistance have on the flow of electric current in a circuit?

....

b) What units is resistance measured in? Circle the correct answer.

ohms   volts   amperes   currents

c) What is the name given to materials that electricity can't easily pass through?

....

Q6   The table shows the **resistance** of three different materials, **A**, **B** and **C**.

Material	Resistance in Ω
A	0.01
B	1
C	0.5

a) Which material is the best conductor? ....

b) How are resistance, potential difference and current linked? Circle the correct answer.

Resistance is equal to   Resistance is equal to   Resistance is equal to
the potential difference   the potential difference   the potential difference
divided by the current.   multiplied by the current.   minus the current.

c) Each material is placed, one at a time, in the circuit shown below.

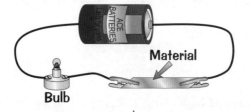

Which material will have the lowest current flowing
through it when it is connected in the circuit?

Remember the higher the
resistance, the harder it is
for current to flow.

....

Measuring Current and Potential Difference

Q1   Preeta measured the **current** flowing around the circuit below using device A.

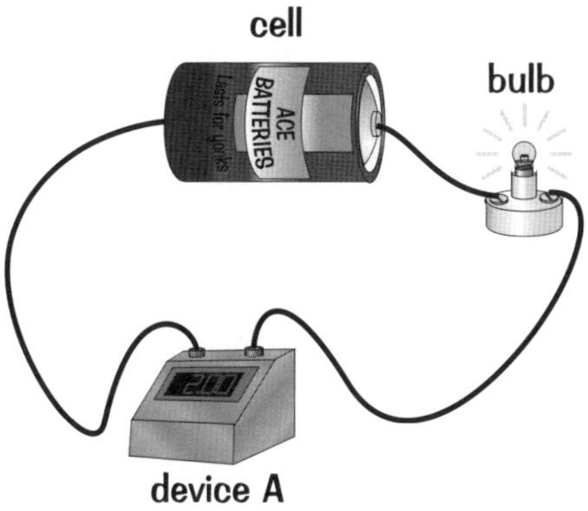

a) What units is current measured in? ....

b) What is **device A** called?

....

c) Device A showed a reading of **2 A**.
What was the **current** flowing through the bulb?

....

cell

bulb

device A

Q2   The symbol of the device used to measure **potential difference** is shown below.

a) What is this device called?

....

b) What units is potential difference measured in?

....

c) Circle the circuit where the device is correctly placed
to measure the potential difference across the bulb.

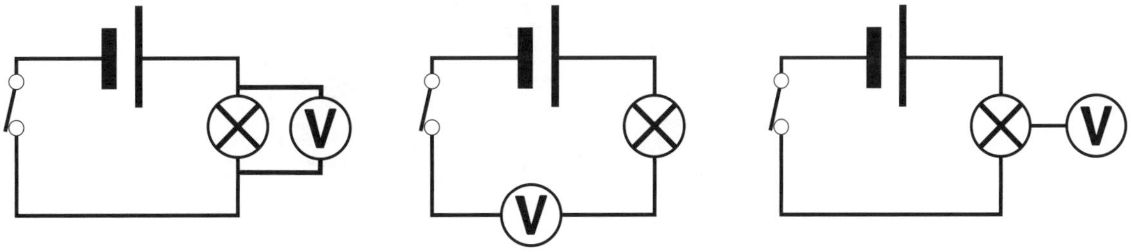

Q3   A bulb is connected to a battery with a **potential difference rating** of 12 V.

a) What does the potential difference rating of the battery mean?

....

b) The bulb has a potential difference rating of 5 V. Is it safe for this bulb
and battery to be connected? Circle the correct answer.

Yes, the potential difference across the bulb needs to be greater than 5 V.	No, the potential difference across the bulb needs to be 5 V or less.	No, the potential difference across the bulb needs to be less than 5 V.

Measuring Current and Potential Difference

Q4 Draw lines to match these components with the correct circuit **symbols**. The first one has been done for you.

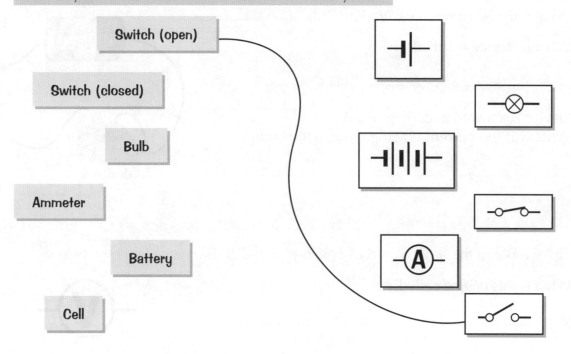

Q5 Vijay made the electrical circuit shown below.

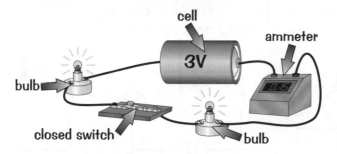

Complete the circuit **diagram** of Vijay's circuit in the box below.

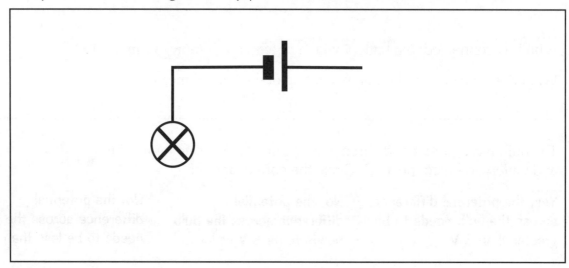

Series and Parallel Circuits

Q1 Lara makes a **series** circuit by attaching a bulb to a battery. The bulb is **lit**. Circle the sentence(s) below that are **true**.

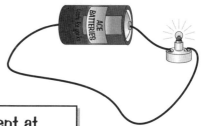

> The current can only travel one way around the circuit.

> The current gives up some of its energy to the bulb.

> The current is different at different points in the circuit.

Q2 Look at the circuit diagram below.

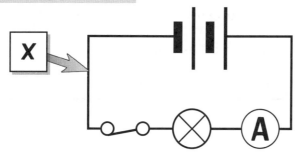

a) Is this circuit a **series** or **parallel** circuit? Explain your answer.

....

....

b) Draw **one arrow** on the diagram to show the direction the current flows around the circuit.

c) The **ammeter** in this circuit reads **2 A**. If you moved the bulb to point X, what would the current flowing through it be? Tick (✔) the correct box.

☐ 0 A   ☐ 2 A   ☐ 1 A   ☐ 4 A

Q3 Look at the circuit diagram on the right. If the switch is opened, which bulbs will be lit? Circle the correct answer.

> Hint: Opening a switch will make a gap in the circuit. Current can only flow when a circuit is complete.

Bulbs A, B and C

All of them

Bulbs D and E

None of them

Bulb E   Bulb A

Bulb D

Bulb C   Bulb B

Series and Parallel Circuits

Q4 This circuit diagram shows a circuit containing **two bulbs**. Say which of the following statements are **true (T)** or **false (F)** by circling the appropriate letter.

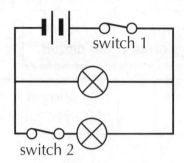

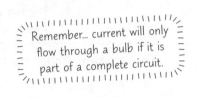

Remember... current will only flow through a bulb if it is part of a complete circuit.

a) The bulbs are connected in parallel.	**(T / F)**
b) The electric current is the same everywhere in the circuit.	**(T / F)**
c) If only switch 1 is open, both bulbs will be off.	**(T / F)**
d) If only switch 2 is open, both bulbs will be off.	**(T / F)**

Q5 The circuit below has **five** bulbs (A, B, C, D and E).

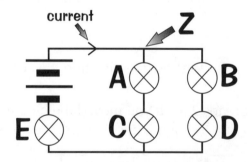

a) What happens to the current in the circuit at point Z?

....

b) For each change to the circuit listed below, show which bulbs would be **on** and which would be **off** by writing the correct letters in the table.

Hint: unscrewing a bulb will cause a gap in the circuit.

Change to original circuit	Bulb(s) on	Bulb(s) off
Bulb A is unscrewed		
Bulb D is unscrewed		
Bulb E is unscrewed		

Series and Parallel Circuits

Q6 The diagram shows the parallel circuit that powers two lights in a garage.

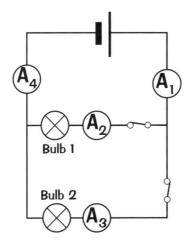

a) In this circuit, ammeter **A₁** reads **10 A** and ammeter **A₂** reads **1 A**.

   i) What will the reading on ammeter A_4 be? ....

   ii) What will the reading on ammeter A_3 be? Circle the correct answer.

| **3 A** | **10 A** | **11 A** | **1 A** | **9 A** |

b) Give **one** reason why connecting the garage lights using a **parallel** circuit is better than connecting them using a **series** circuit.

....

....

....

Q7 Fill in the **three** missing values of current on the circuit diagram below.

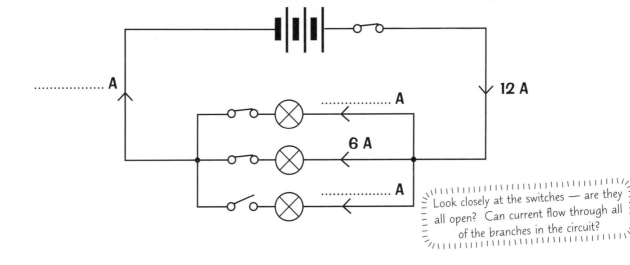

.... A

12 A

6 A

.... A

.... A

Look closely at the switches — are they all open? Can current flow through all of the branches in the circuit?

Static Electricity

Q1 Complete the sentences by circling the correct words in the brackets.

a) Atoms contain positive and negative (**atoms** / **charges**).

b) Electrons are the (**positive** / **negative**) parts of atoms.

c) (**Electrons** / **Positive charges**) can move, but (**electrons** / **positive charges**) can't.

d) Electrons can be (**transferred** / **reflected**) when two insulating objects are rubbed together.

e) When an object gains electrons, it becomes (**negatively** / **positively**) charged.

f) An object that (**gains** / **loses**) electrons is left with a positive charge.

Q2 A teacher demonstrates static electricity by rubbing a **plastic rod** with a **cloth**. The rod becomes **negatively** charged.

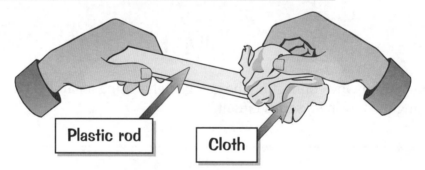

Plastic rod

Cloth

a) Complete this sentence using the words given below.

electrons   rod   cloth

.... are scraped off the ....

and left on the ....

b) For each sentence below, put a tick (✔) in the correct box to show whether it's **true** or **false**.

                                                                 True   **False**

i) After rubbing, the cloth will have the same charge as the rod.

ii) After rubbing, the cloth will have the opposite charge to the rod.

iii)The cloth and the rod will attract each other after rubbing.

iv)The cloth and the rod will repel each other after rubbing.

Static Electricity

Q3 The force between charged objects depends on what type of **charge** they have.

a) Tick the box next to the **true** sentence below.

☐ Charged objects need to touch each other to feel a force.

☐ Charged objects don't need to touch each other to feel a force.

b) Complete the table by writing **attraction** or **repulsion** in each gap.

Charge of object 1	Charge of object 2	Force between objects
Positive	Positive	
Positive	Negative	
Negative	Positive	
Negative	Negative	

c) Use your table to complete this sentence.

Opposite charges ....,

charges of the same type ....

Q4 As Abu walks along a carpet, the carpet and the soles of his shoes rub together. The **carpet** becomes **positively** charged and the soles of his **shoes** become **negatively** charged.

a) What is the name of this type of charge? Circle the correct answer.

static charge   dynamic charge   current

b) Abu says 'Positive charges were transferred from the soles of my shoes to the carpet.' Explain why Abu is **wrong**.

....

....

Static Electricity

Q5 Nena rubbed a red balloon on her head. The **balloon** became **negatively** charged and her hair became **positively** charged. When she held the balloon **near** her head, her hair moved towards the balloon.

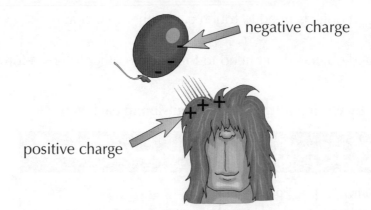

negative charge

positive charge

a) The balloon and Nena's hair each have an electric field. What is an **electric field**?

....

....

b) Draw an arrow on the diagram to show the direction electrons were transferred between Nena's hair and the balloon when they were rubbed together.

c) Complete the sentences below to explain why Nena's hair moved towards the balloon by circling the correct words in the brackets.

> The charge on Nena's hair is the (**same** / **opposite**) type as the charge on
>
> the balloon. This means the hair is (**attracted to** / **repelled by**) the balloon.

d) Nena puts the balloon down, but notices a lot of the hairs on her head are still standing up. The picture below shows a few of these hairs.

Hair

Explain why these hairs stand up like this.

Hint: Remember each hair is charged...

....

....

Magnets

Q1 The diagram below shows the **magnetic field** around a magnet.

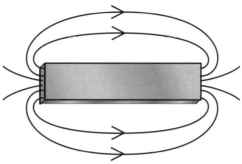

a) What is the name given to the type of **magnet** shown in the diagram?

....

b) What are the **lines** on the diagram called?

....

c) What is a magnetic field? Tick the box next to the correct answer.

☐ The region where magnetic materials experience a force.

☐ The region where magnetic materials experience a charge.

☐ The region where magnetic materials experience a current.

d) Mark the **North** and **South** poles on the diagram above by writing **N** and **S** on the correct ends of the magnet.

Q2 Complete this paragraph about compasses using the words below.

magnetic   North pole   maps   north   line up

Unless it is next to a magnet, a compass will ....
with the Earth's .... field. The compass will
point to the Earth's magnetic ....
.... always show which direction is
.... on them, so you can use them with a
compass to find your way.

Magnets

Q3   This question is about **forces** between magnets.

a)   Write down whether you think each sentence is **true** or **false**.

i) A N-pole will repel a S-pole. ....

ii) A N-pole will attract a S-pole. ....

iii) A S-pole will attract a S-pole. ....

iv) A S-pole will attract a N-pole. ....

Ugh...
how repulsive

b)   Complete this sentence by circling the correct words in the brackets.

> Magnets (**need to** / **do not need to**) touch for there to be a force between them.

Q4   Ibrahim put some **compasses** near a magnet as shown in the diagram below.

a)   Which **direction** do these compasses point in? Circle the correct answer.

> From the North pole of the magnet to South pole of the magnet, along the magnetic field lines.

> Towards the North pole of the magnet.

> Towards the South pole of the magnet.

> From the South pole of the magnet to the North pole of the magnet, along the magnetic field lines.

b)   On the diagram, draw an **arrow** in each empty circle to show which way each **compass** is pointing.

I remember when this was all fields...

Electromagnets

Q1   The diagram below shows an **electromagnet**. Why is the
electromagnet magnetic? Tick the box next to the correct answer.

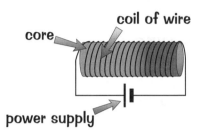

| | Electric current going through the wire causes a magnetic field around it. |

☐   Electric current going through the wire causes a magnetic field around it.

☐   The core of the electromagnet is a bar magnet.

☐   The power supply is magnetic. The wire becomes magnetic
because it is touching another magnetic material.

Q2   The diagram below shows the **magnetic field** around
an **electromagnet** connected to a power supply.

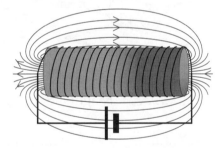

a)   Which kind of **magnet** has the same magnetic field as the long coil of wire?

....

b)   What would happen to the magnetic field of the electromagnet
if the power supply was turned off?

....

....

c)   What is the **core** of an electromagnet usually made from? Circle the correct answer.

a bar magnet   soft iron   soft copper   soft steel   rubber

Electromagnets

Q3 Circle the **two** changes below you could make to an electromagnet to **increase** its strength.

Decrease the current in the wire

Have fewer turns on the coil

Increase the current in the wire

Have more turns on the coil

Q4 The diagram shows an **electric motor**. Show where each part is on the diagram by writing the correct letter next to its name below.

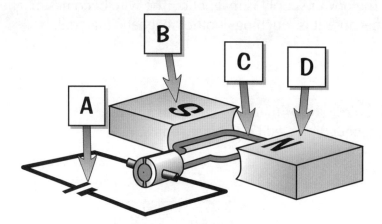

Loop of coiled wire — .... 　　Magnet (South pole) — ....

Magnet (North pole) — .... 　　Cell — ....

Q5 Joel works in a scrap yard. He uses an **electromagnet** to lift scrap metal from one part of the scrap yard and drop it in another part of the scrap yard.

Why are electromagnets **better** for this job than normal magnets?

....

....

....

....

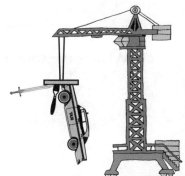

Electromagnets

Q6 The propellor on Cate's model aeroplane is powered by the **electric motor** shown below.

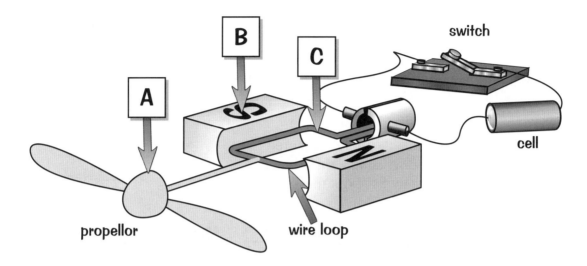

a) The electric motor contains an **electromagnet**. Which label, **A**, **B** or **C**, points to the electromagnet in the propeller motor? Circle the correct answer below.

b) Complete this passage to explain why the propellor spins when the switch is closed. Use the words given in the boxes.

magnetic field	force	magnetic
current	magnets	wire loop

When the switch is closed a ....

flows through the .... The wire loop

becomes .... The loop is already in

a .... because it is between two

.... This means the loop feels a

.... which makes the loop turn.

The propellor is attached to the loop of wire, so it turns as well.

Gravity

Q1 Abbie is using a **newton meter** to measure the **weight** of a metal disc.

newton meter

metal disc

a) What **units** is weight usually measured in?

....

b) Name the **force** that causes objects to have weight.

....

c) After measuring the weight, Abbie measured the **mass** of the metal disc using a mass balance. Tick (✔) the **three** statements about mass that are **true**.

☐ The mass of an object never changes.

☐ Mass is a force.

☐ Mass is the same thing as weight.

☐ Mass is the same as gravity.

☐ Mass is measured in kilograms.

☐ Mass is the amount of 'stuff' in an object.

Q2 These facts about **gravity** have got all mixed up. Draw **lines** to match the beginning of each sentence with its end. The first one has been done for you.

Anything with mass will attract...

The Earth and the Moon are...

The attraction between the Earth and the Sun is bigger than...

Gravitational field strength is...

The attraction between two objects because of their masses...

...is called gravity.

...the attraction between the Earth and the Moon.

...anything else with mass.

...attracted to each other.

...how strong gravity is.

Gravity

Q3   Complete these sentences using the words given below.

bigger   force   stronger   gravity

> The .... of .... between
> two objects depends on their masses. The ....
> their masses are, the .... it will be.

Q4   The fact sheet below shows some information about a space robot.

Ace Space Robot

Mass — 1000 kg

Weight the wheels can support before breaking — 20 000 N

Colour — Hot pink

a)   Calculate the weight of the robot on Earth.

....

....

b)   The robot is going to be sent to a planet with a gravitational field strength of **100 N/kg**.

   i) What will the mass of the robot be on this planet?

....

   ii) How much will the robot weigh on this planet? Circle the correct answer.

   | 1000 N | | 1 N | | 100 000 N | | 100 N |

   iii) Explain why the robot should not be sent to this planet.   *Hint: Look at the fact sheet, will the robot work when it gets there?*

....

....

....

74

The Sun and Stars

Q1   The **Earth** is one of the planets that moves around the Sun.

a)   What is the Sun? Circle the correct answer.

a star   a galaxy   a planet   a Milky Way

b)   What is the path that a planet follows around the Sun called?

....

c)   What shape is the path of a planet around the Sun?

....

d)   What is the main difference between stars and planets?

....

....

Q2   The Earth is in the **Milky Way**.

a)   What is the **Milky Way**?

....

b)   What else can be found in the Milky Way? Circle the correct answer.

The Universe   Billions of galaxies   The Sun   Hundreds of universes

c)   Tick (✔) how many stars there are in the Milky Way.

HUNDREDS ☐   THOUSANDS ☐   MILLIONS ☐   BILLIONS ☐

d)   Tick (✔) how many galaxies there are in the Universe.

HUNDREDS ☐   THOUSANDS ☐   MILLIONS ☐   BILLIONS ☐

The Sun and Stars

Q3   **Proxima Centauri** is one of the stars in our galaxy.

a)   Circle the correct word(s) in the brackets to complete this sentence.

Proxima Centauri is the (**furthest** / **second closest** / **closest**) star to the Earth.

b)   Proxima Centauri is about **4 light years** away from the Earth.

i)   What is meant by a **light year**?

....

....

ii) How **long** has it taken the light from Proxima Centauri to reach the Earth?

....

Q4   Astronomers use light years to measure **distances**. Explain why it would not be sensible to measure your height in light years.

....

....

....

Q5   Complete the crossword using the clues below. The numbers in the brackets show you how many letters the missing words have.

Across

2. The name of the path of the Earth around the Sun. (5)
3. The planet that we live on. (5)
5. The galaxy that Earth is in. (5, 3)

Down

1. A unit of distance in space. (5, 4)
4. The Sun is one of these. (4)

Day and Night and the Four Seasons

Q1 Use the words on the right to complete the sentences below.

| four axis summer nights |
| seasons winter year days |

a) The Earth spins on its ....

b) It takes a .... for the Earth to orbit the Sun once.

c) The tilt of the Earth's axis causes the ....

d) In summer, ... last longer than ....

e) There are .... seasons every year.

f) In ...., the sunlight is stronger.

g) The days are always shortest in the ....

Q2 The diagram on the right shows the Earth in its orbit during early **January**. Use the diagram to answer these questions.

a) Is it **night** time or **day** time in Britain in the diagram?

....

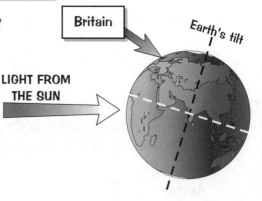

Britain

Earth's tilt

LIGHT FROM THE SUN

b) Is it **winter** or **summer** in Britain in the diagram?

....

c) Is Britain in the **northern** or **southern hemisphere**?

....

Hint: Think about the Earth's tilt...

d) Explain why the days are **longer** and **warmer** in the **summer** in Britain.

....

....

....

....

Section 5 — The Earth and Beyond